When you're ready, say...

"Alexa, open Readyland!"

Works with any Alexa-enabled device or the Alexa app.

NEED HELP?

For help with parental permissions, or any other issues, visit

www.readyland.com/setup

or scan this QR code.

Still need help? Contact support@readyland.com.

NAVIGATION

To hear something again ➤	"Alexa, repeat."
To skip to the next page ➤	"Alexa, skip."
To move to a page ➤	"Alexa, go to page…"
To change books ➤	"Alexa, change books."
To exit the skill ➤	"Alexa, stop."

Readyland™

Copyright © 2023 by Readyland LLC
Amazon, Echo, Alexa, and all related logos are trademarks of Amazon.com, Inc. or its affiliates.

Published in the United States of America by Readyland LLC, 2023

ISBN: 979-8-9853108-8-7
Printed in China
Visit our website at www.readyland.com

Readyland Presents

OWL & DRAGON™

A Magical Adventure

Far away, in a nest way up high, Owl is getting ready for the night. Even with the moon bright in the sky, Owl thinks the dark is a little scary.

1

Suddenly, Owl hears a loud noise and
sees a scary shape flying above the forest.

"Who's there?"

I'm
Ready

Thankfully, it's Owl's friend, Dragon!

"I didn't mean to frighten you. I just came by to see
if you want to come explore the forest with me!"

"I don't know, Dragon.
Even though I'm an owl,
I'm scared of the dark! Let
me just grab my flashlight."

"You don't need a light, I'm learning how to breathe fire! Come with me and we can explore together."

"OK, Dragon, I'll try."

"Owl, you can do this! I believe in you!"

4

Before long, they're at a beautiful pond with musical sounds all around.

5

"You did it, Owl! This is my favorite place. Sometimes I even come here and sing. Do you want to sing with me?"

Owl nods.

6

Their song unexpectedly opens a magical portal. Dragon wants to dive right in, but Owl doesn't think it's a good idea.

I'm Ready

"Come on, Owl! It'll be fun!"

Dragon reaches for Owl's wing and they jump into the mysterious opening together.

Whoosh! The portal transports them deeper into the forest. They arrive in the Glowing Everglades, where magical, glowing flowers cast colorful shadows.

9

"Uh, Dragon.... What's that big, red shadow?"

Luckily, it's just a wise old gnome who wants to help them on their journey.

11

"Choose a path and be on your way."

Sparkles surround Owl and Dragon as they enter Fairy Corner for the first time.

I'm Ready

13

Fairies of all shapes and sizes sprinkle
magical dust on them as they walk, making
them glitter and glow from head to toe.

14

The fairies lead them to a dark, underground cavern. Owl and Dragon are shining bright from the fairy dust and can see everything around them. They stop to admire the shimmering crystals.

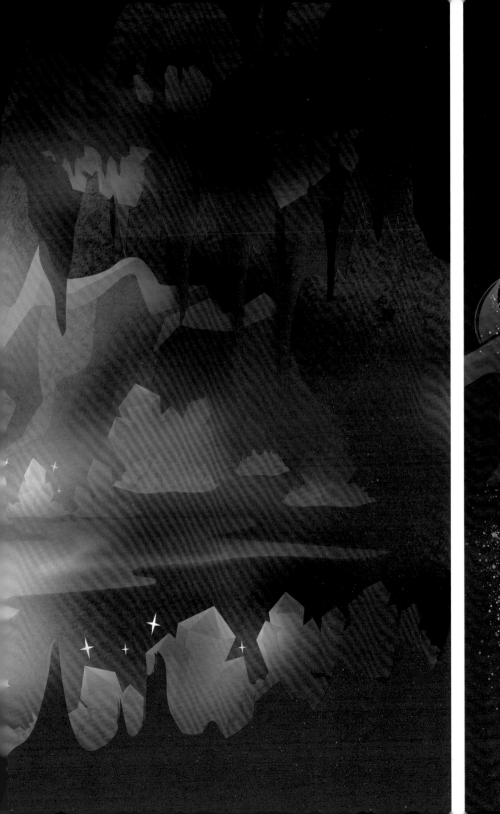

"Uh-oh, Dragon! I think we've been here too long... our fairy dust is fading."

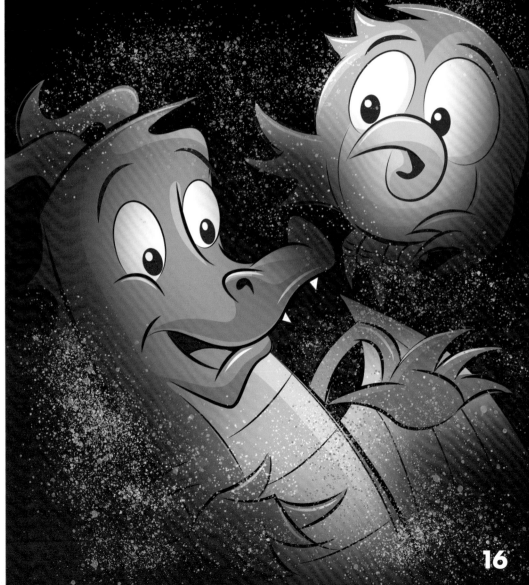

Suddenly, it's pitch dark! For the first time during their adventure, Dragon doesn't know what to do.

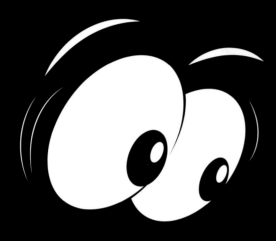

"Oh no! How will we find our way out now?"

"It's okay, Dragon. You can light the way with your fire, remember?"

"But I can only make a little one."

"Dragon, you can do this. I believe in you!"

18

The fire lights up everything around them, revealing some glowing tunnels.

20

Owl leads Dragon through the tunnel and out into the moonlit sky.

"We made it, Dragon!"

Up ahead, Dragon sees Owl's nest. They
flap their wings and off they go, waving
goodbye to the enchanted forest below.

Back at home, Owl smiles.

"I never thought I'd say this, Dragon,
but I can't wait for our next adventure!"

25

THE END

Ready for more?

Find these inside this book!

Explore with Alexa

More from Readyland

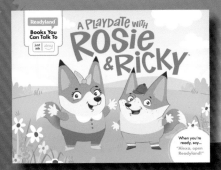

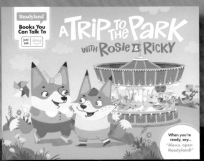

Visit Readyland.com for a complete list of our books

Try this!

Say, "Alexa, what are Owl and Dragon doing now?"

Other things you can try!

- "Alexa, tell me a joke!"
- "Alexa, set a timer!"
- "Alexa, what's the weather?"
- "Alexa, how many planets are there?"

...and so much more!